Mystery Mob
and the
Ghost Town

Roger Hurn

Illustrated by
Stik

Rising Stars UK Ltd.
7 Hatchers Mews, Bermondsey Street, London SE1 3GS
www.risingstars-uk.com

The right of Roger Hurn to be identified as the author of this work
has been asserted by him in accordance with the Copyright,
Design and Patents Act 1988.

Published 2008
Reprinted 2013

Text, design and layout © Rising Stars UK Ltd.

Cover design: Burville-Riley Partnership
Illustrator: Stik, Bill Greenhead for Illustration Ltd
Text design and typesetting: Andy Wilson
Publisher: Gill Budgell
Editor: Catherine Baker

British Library Cataloguing in Publication Data.
A CIP record for this book is available from the British Library

ISBN: 978-1-84680-423-6

Printed in the UK by Ashford Colour Press Ltd.

MIX
Paper from
responsible sources
FSC® C011748

Contents

Meet the Mystery Mob

Name:

Gummy

FYI: Gummy hasn't got much brain – and even fewer teeth.

Loves: Soup.

Hates: Toffee chews.

Fact: The brightest thing about him is his shirt.

Name:

Lee

FYI: If Lee was any cooler he'd be a cucumber.

Loves: Hip-hop.

Hates: Hopscotch.

Fact: He has his own designer label (which he peeled off a tin).

Name:

FYI: Rob lives in his own world – he's just visiting planet Earth.

Loves: Daydreaming.

Hates: Nightmares.

Fact: Rob always does his homework – he just forgets to write it down.

Name:

Dwayne

FYI: Dwayne is smarter than a tree full of owls.

Loves: Anything complicated.

Hates: Join-the-dots books.

Fact: If he was any brighter you could use him as a floodlight at football matches.

Name:

Chet

FYI: Chet is as brave as a lion with steel jaws.

Loves: Having adventures.

Hates: Knitting.

Fact: He's as tough as the chicken his granny cooks for his tea.

Name:

Adi

FYI: Adi is as happy as a football fan with tickets to the big match.

Loves: Telling jokes.

Hates: Moaning minnies.

Fact: He knows more jokes than a jumbo joke book.

① The Gold Rush

The Mystery Mob are on holiday in the USA. They go to see Cactus Canyon, an old Wild West ghost town.

Rob   I bet we'll see some ghosts if we keep our eyes peeled!

Just then Jess and Jim, two friendly Park Rangers, come up. It's their job to look after the town.

Jess   Hi guys! Enjoying your visit to Cactus Canyon?

Lee   Yeah – it's cool. But why's it called a ghost town?

Jim   Because nobody lives here any more.

Lee   Why did they all leave?

Rob   (excitedly) 'Cos the ghosts scared them away!

The two Rangers laugh. They tell
the Mystery Mob that there used to be
gold mines in the town. The people left
when the gold ran out.

Rob   But are there any real ghosts
            living here?

Ranger Jim grins. He points at a poster
by the entrance to an old gold mine.

This gold mine belonged to
HAIRY HANK

Hank blew himself up with
dynamite by accident when he
was digging for gold back in 1849.

R.I.P.

Jim   Some people think the ghost of Hairy Hank haunts this old mine.

Lee   Cool.

Rob   But has anyone ever seen him?

Jess   Well, I think I saw him once, going into the mine. But it was dark at the time, so I can't be sure.

Lee   Didn't you chase after him?

Rob   Yeah. I'd have gone down the mine after him.

Lee   No way. You're scared of your own shadow, Rob.

Rob   True, but that's only 'cos my shadow's pretty scary!

Jess   By the time I got to the mouth of the mine, he'd vanished.

Jim   It was all in your mind, Jess! Anyway, no one ever goes into Hairy Hank's mine.

Lee   Why's that?

Jim   Well, there's nothing to see down there. It's boring.

Rob   Hmmm. I bet no one goes there because they don't want to come face-to-face with Hairy Hank's ghost!

Lee   But did Hairy Hank find any gold in his mine before he blew himself up?

Jim   Nobody knows. Hank didn't live to tell.

Jess   But anyway, if there *is* any gold down there it belongs to the US government. They own the mine now.

The Mystery Mob can't wait to explore Cactus Canyon. They rush off. They are sure they'll find some gold somewhere – and maybe a ghost or two!

2

All That Glitters

Rob and Lee are walking
past the entrance to
Hairy Hank's old mine
when Lee sees something.
He stops to take a closer look.

Lee   Hey, Rob, there's something fishy
going on here.

Rob   Don't be silly, Lee. Nobody goes
fishing in a gold mine – unless it's
for goldfish!

Lee   Very funny, Rob – not!

Rob   Okay, what is it?

Lee   Well, the Rangers said nobody
ever goes into the mine –
but someone has.

Rob   How do you know?

Lee   Look, there are footprints
in the dust, and they lead
in and out of the mine.

Rob   Hey, you're right. Ooooooh,
this is so creepy. Do you think
Hairy Hank's ghost made
the footprints?

Lee   No, ghosts don't make footprints.
But I reckon Hairy Hank
must have found gold
before he died – and now a
crook is stealing it!

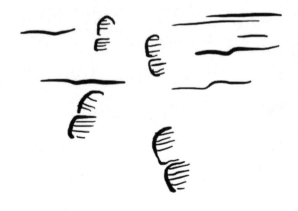

Rob The crook must be mad.

Lee Why?

Rob Because the mine's haunted.
Jess said so.

Lee Well, we're still going to go inside
and take a look.

Rob But shouldn't we tell the Rangers?

Lee Look, Rob, it can't do any harm
if we just take a quick peek.
And then, if we find out anything,
we'll go and fetch Jess and Jim.

Rob   Well, I don't know.

Lee   Aw, come on, Rob.
We're wasting time.

Rob   Okay. Let's do it!
Hey, do you think we'll find
some gold nuggets in the mine?

Lee   (sighing) No, I think we'll find
some *chicken* nuggets. Duh!
It's a gold mine, Rob, of course
we're going to find gold.
Now come on.

Rob and Lee sneak into the mine.

Rob   I don't like it in here, Lee.
It's a bit dark.

Lee   Don't worry, we'll be fine.
I've got my torch. Just don't
make any loud noises.

Rob   Yeah – we don't want the crook
to hear us.

Lee   It's not just that – loud noises
can start a whopping great
rockfall. The last thing we need
is for the roof to cave in and a ton
of rocks to land on top of us.

Rob   Gulp! I'm going to walk on tiptoe from now on.

Lee   Good idea. And I'm going to switch on my torch. If you see any gold glittering, give me a shout.

Rob   Er … didn't you just say not to make any loud noises?

Lee   Rob, why do I get the feeling that the only gold you'll find is Fool's Gold?

Rob   What's Fool's Gold?

Lee   A yellow metal that looks like gold. It's called Fool's Gold because it fools some people.

Rob   That's okay. I don't fool easily.

Lee   Really? So how come you once tried to eat soup with chopsticks?

Rob   Because we were in a Chinese restaurant.

Lee just shakes his head. The two boys go deeper and deeper into the mine.

Rob   (whispering) Hey, Lee.
There's something glittering
in the rock wall over here.

Lee   Yes, but you know what they say:
'All that glitters is not gold'.

Rob   Right, but this is glittering
and it *is* gold.

Lee   Wow, you're right. It's the real deal! And look, here's a pick-axe and a wheelbarrow. Someone's been using them to dig out the gold and cart it off. It must be the crook.

Rob picks up a strange object that was lying on a rock.

Rob   Hey – what's this?

Lee   Yikes!

Rob   What's the matter?

Lee   That's a stick of dynamite!
Put it down now. And Rob,
please do it gently.

Before Rob can put the dynamite down,
someone appears. He's wearing a huge
cowboy hat and most of his face
is covered by a big bushy beard.

Rob   Arghhhh! It's the ghost
of Hairy Hank!

③

Fool's Gold

Hairy Hank looks
really scary.
Rob and Lee are
in big trouble.

Hairy Hank

Boys, this sure is your unlucky
day. You never should have
messed with Hairy Hank.

Rob But what do you want gold for,
Mr Hairy Hank? You're a ghost.

Lee He's no ghost. He's a crook
pretending to be Hairy Hank.

Rob No way! Well, he had me fooled.

Lee And that's *so* not easy to do.

Rob   Exactly! Er … but how do you know he's not a ghost?

Lee   Well, the mobile phone on his belt is a bit of a clue.

Rob   Gotcha! But who is he really?

Hairy Hank

You'll never know. I'm going to tie you both up and leave you at the bottom of the mine shaft. By the time anybody finds you I'll be long gone – with the gold!

Hairy Hank moves towards the boys.
Rob yells out in terror.

Lee   Hang on a minute.
         What's that sound?

Rob   It's the sound of my knees
         knocking together in fright.

Lee   No. It's the sound of rocks falling.
         Your shout must have shaken
         them loose. Look out! The roof
         of the mine is falling down!

Lee and Rob dive for cover under
the wheelbarrow. They make it in
the nick of time, but a large rock hits
Hairy Hank on the head. He's knocked
out cold. When the rocks stop falling,
the boys poke their heads out
from beneath the wheelbarrow.

Rob   Hey, we look like a two-headed
           tortoise, but at least we're
           still alive!

Lee   Yeah, but we're also trapped.

Rob   What do you mean?
           Hairy Hank's out for the count,
           so what's to stop us from
           just walking out of here
           and bringing the Rangers
           back to arrest him?

Lee   Those rocks.

Lee shines his torch back down
the tunnel. There's a huge pile of rocks
blocking the way back out of the mine.
Things are really not looking good.

The Big Bang

The boys check out Hairy Hank
to make sure he isn't badly hurt.

Rob   Hey, look at this, Lee.
        Hairy Hank's wearing a
        false beard.

Lee   Is he now? Well, let's take it off
        and see who he really is.

Rob and Lee grab Hairy Hank's beard
and tug hard. The beard comes away
in their hands.

Rob   (in surprise) It's Jim,
the friendly Ranger!

Lee   Huh. And I thought he was
one of the good guys.
Still, I'll use his mobile
to call for help.

Rob   Great idea!

Lee takes the phone.

Lee   Oh no. There's no signal.

Jim groans loudly and begins to stir.

Lee Uh-oh! Jim's waking up.

Rob Don't worry. He dropped his gun
when the rock hit him. I'll grab it.

Lee Be careful with that gun, Rob.
It may go off.

Rob No, it won't. I'm not that clumsy.
Whoops!

Rob trips and pulls the trigger.
A flame shoots out of the barrel.

Rob   Phew! Thank goodness it's not a real gun. It's only a lighter.

Lee   Yes, but it's lit the fuse on that stick of dynamite.

Rob   What stick of dynamite?

Lee   The one you've still got in your hand.

Rob blows on the fuse. This makes it burn even faster.

Rob   Arrrrrgh! I can't put it out!

Lee   Quick, Rob. Throw it away.

Rob   But where shall I throw it?

Lee   As far away from us as you can, you dummy!

The dynamite lands on the rock pile. Jim stands up. He's a bit groggy.

Jim   Now you two are for it.

Rob   Don't move. I've got you covered
            with this gun.

Jim   Nice try, kid, but that gun
            is a fake.

Lee   Yes, but the dynamite isn't.

Jim   Dynamite? What dynamite?

Rob   The dynamite right behind you.
            Duck!

Once again Rob and Lee dive under the wheelbarrow. There is a gi-normous explosion.

When the dust settles, Jim is looking very sorry for himself. His face is black with smoke. His hat and clothes have been blown off and he's standing in his tattered vest and underpants.

Lee   Are you okay, Rob?

Rob   I'm fine, but I'm not so sure about Jim. I think he's seeing stars.

Lee   Forget about him. The dynamite has blasted the rock pile out of the way. Come on. Let's escape while Jim is too dizzy to stop us.

5

A Fair Cop

The boys race up to the entrance
of the mine. They bump into Jess.
She's heard the explosion and has come
to find out what's going on.

Jess   I heard a loud bang coming from
the mine. Are you boys okay?

Lee   We're fine.

Jess   Well, that's good – I thought
you were in trouble.

Lee   Jim's the one in trouble, not us.

Rob   That's right. He's a crook.

Lee   He's been stealing gold
from Hairy Hank's mine.

Rob   And he's been dressing up
as the ghost of Hairy Hank.

Lee   He did it to scare people so they
would keep away from the mine.

Rob   Yeah. He didn't want anyone
to see him sneaking the gold out.

Jess   Grrr! That no-good son of a gun.
Where is he now?

Lee   He's still down there.
            But he won't come out.

Jess   Why not? Because he knows
            I'll arrest him?

Rob   No. Because he's lost his trousers!

Jess goes down into the mine to arrest Jim.

Rob   Wow, we've had lots of excitement
            today, Lee.

Lee   We sure have. In fact, it's been
            a blast!

About the author

Roger Hurn has:

- had a hit record in Turkey
- won *The Weakest Link* on TV
- swum with sharks on the Great Barrier Reef.

Now he's a writer, and he hopes you like reading about the Mystery Mob as much as he likes writing about them.

Wild West quiz

Questions

1 Which famous Wild West US Marshall had bad wind?

2 How do you know the Indians were the first people in North America?

3 What do you call a cowboy who wins second prize in a gun fight?

4 What did the cowboy say to the horse next door?

5 Why did the cowboy die with his boots on?

6 Why did the cowboy's pony have to gargle?

7 A cowboy rides into town on Friday. He stays for only two days and then leaves on Friday. How?

8 Why did the cowboy sleep with all the lights on?

How did you score?

☝ If you got all eight Wild West answers correct, then you are a rootin', tootin', six-gun shootin' cowboy!

☝ If you got six Wild West answers correct, then you're all saddled up and ready to ride 'em, cowboy.

☝ If you got fewer than four Wild West answers correct, then you are more Mild West than Wild West.

41

When I was a kid

Question When you were a kid, did you want to be a cowboy?

Roger Yes, so my mum bought me a really cool cowboy outfit.

Question What did your mates say?

Roger They said it didn't fit me.

Question Why was that?

Roger Because I was acting too big for my boots!

Question Okay, but did you all play cowboys?

Roger Too right! We had a cowboy camp.

Question That sounds like fun.

Roger It wasn't. It was too windy for us to sleep in our tent.

Question Oh, so you had bad weather?

Roger No. We had too many baked beans at our cowboy camp fire barbeque!

Adi's favourite Wild West joke

What do you call a dinosaur that wears a cowboy hat and cowboy boots, and shoots a six-gun?

Tyrannosaurus Tex!

How to be a gold miner

 Don't keep your dynamite next to the camp fire – unless you want to go out with a bang!

 If you're going panning for gold in the Wild West, get your supplies from Pan Francisco.

 Make sure you go panning for gold – not mould. One's yellow and expensive, the other's yukky and smelly.

 When you go to your gold mine, try to avoid the gold rush hour.

Make sure you call your gold mine
'The Rainbow', because you always find
gold at the end of the rainbow.

Take a vacuum cleaner with you to your
mine – you'll need it to hoover up
the gold dust.

Five fantastic facts about Wild West cowboys

1 A cowboy always made sure his horse was fed and watered before he went to get his own meal.

2 A cowboy never tried on another cowboy's hat.

3 When approaching someone from behind, a cowboy always gave a loud greeting before he got within pistol shot.

4 Cowboys would swear and cuss in front of men, horses and cows, but never in front of women.

5 When cowboys left a town after a weekend of partying they shot their six-guns into the air, whooped like crazy and rode their horses as fast as they could. They called this 'hurrahing' the town.

Wild West lingo

Chaps A type of leather over-trousers worn by cowboys, not a posh name for a group of men.

Cowpoke This is a Wild West name for a man who looks after cattle – it is nothing to do with prodding cows with your finger.

Gunslinger A gunslinger was a cowboy who liked to fight with guns – not someone who likes throwing them as far as he can.

Quick on the draw This means being able to pull your gun out of its holster very quickly in a gun fight. It doesn't mean an artist who works fast.

Shakin' a hoof This means dancing. It's not what you do when introduced to a horse.

Mystery Mob

Mystery Mob Set 1:

Mystery Mob and the Abominable Snowman
Mystery Mob and the Big Match
Mystery Mob and the Circus of Doom
Mystery Mob and the Creepy Castle
Mystery Mob and the Haunted Attic
Mystery Mob and the Hidden Treasure
Mystery Mob and the Magic Bottle
Mystery Mob and the Missing Millions
Mystery Mob and the Monster on the Moor
Mystery Mob and the Mummy's Curse
Mystery Mob and the Time Machine
Mystery Mob and the UFO

Mystery Mob Set 2:

Mystery Mob and the Ghost Town
Mystery Mob and the Bonfire Night Plot
Mystery Mob and the April Fools' Day Joker
Mystery Mob and the Great Pancake Day Race
Mystery Mob and the Scary Santa
Mystery Mob and the Conker Conspiracy
Mystery Mob and the Top Talent Contest
Mystery Mob and the Night in the Waxworks
Mystery Mob and the Runaway Train
Mystery Mob and the Wrong Robot
Mystery Mob and the Day of the Dinosaurs
Mystery Mob and the Man-eating Tiger

Mystery Mob books are available from most booksellers.

**For mail order information
please call Rising Stars on 0800 091 1602
or visit www.risingstars-uk.com**